Sweet Treat
Algo muy rico

by Deborah Schecter

ISBN: 978-1-338-70294-1
Illustrated by Anne Kennedy
Copyright © 2020 by Deborah Schecter. All rights reserved.
Published by Scholastic Inc., 557 Broadway, New York, NY 10012

10 9 8 7 6   68   23 24 25 26/0

Printed in Jiaxing, China. First printing, June 2020.

■ SCHOLASTIC

I add the banana.

Yo pongo el plátano.

You add the ice cream.

Tú pones el helado.

I add the chocolate.

Yo pongo el chocolate.

You add the whipped cream.

Tú pones la crema batida.

I add the nuts.

Yo pongo las nueces.

You add the cherries.

Tú pones las cerezas.

We share dessert!

¡Nosotros compartimos el postre!